Crossroads of Character:

Learning to Make Wise Choices

by Kate Boyer Brown and Marilyn Boyer

Photography by Kate Boyer Brown

A special thanks to Mary Ann Edman for her expertise and creativity in cover, design, and her commitment to excellence in editing work.

First printing April 2010
Second printing June 2011
Third printing July 2012
Fourth printing March 2014
Fifth printing April 2015
Sixth printing March 2016
Seventh printing April 2020
Eighth Printing June 2020

ISBN 978-0-9777685-2-3

Published by the Learning Parent
2430 Sunnymeade Road
Rustburg, VA 24588
www.thelearningparent.com

Proudly printed in the United States of America by Jostens

OBEDIENCE

doing what is expected of me cheerfully, immediately, and thoroughly

"Children, obey your parents in all things for this is well pleasing unto the Lord." –Colossians 3:20

Luke and Adam were excited about visiting the farm and riding their granddad's horses. Granddad had promised some fun surprises, and the boys couldn't wait to get started!

Luke and Adam said goodbye to their moms as they dropped them off at the farm. "Remember to obey whatever Granddad tells you," Mommy reminded Adam. "Okay, Mom!" Adam called back, waving to his mom as he walked toward Granddad.

"Hello, boys!" Granddad said. "How would you two like a ride on the tractor?" "Oh, yeah!" they shouted together.

“Okay,” said Granddad. “I’ll go get the tractor and come drive around to pick you up. But listen, boys—make sure you stay away from the fence where the horses are. The fence is electric, so it would hurt you badly if you touch it. And I don’t want you around the horses unless I’m with you, because they get spooked easily. They don’t like noise. Do you understand?” “Yes, Granddad,” they both promised.

Granddad headed off to get the tractor from the barn, and the boys amused themselves playing hide and seek near the house. Soon they grew bored though, and started down the lane to see if they could catch a glimpse of Granddad coming on the tractor.

Just then, Luke heard one of the horses snorting not far away. “Look, Adam!” he pointed out. “The horses came to see us! Want to go feed them some grass?” “Yeah!” Adam agreed excitedly, but then he remembered what Granddad had said.

“Oh, wait, Luke. Remember? Granddad said we can’t go near the horses. He said we might spook them. Don’t you think we ought to obey him?” Luke looked thoughtful. “Yeah, you’re right,” he said. “Okay. We’ll just wait for Granddad then.”

Soon Granddad came driving up on the tractor. He turned the tractor off and got down to help the boys up on the seat. When they were all on the tractor, Granddad told the boys, “Adam and Luke, I saw you trying to decide whether to go over near the horses or not, and I’m very pleased you chose to obey. You didn't grumble about it, either—you obeyed cheerfully! I'm glad you chose to do right. And after we go for a ride on the tractor, guess what we're going to do next?"

"What, Granddad?" asked Luke excitedly.

"Ride the horses!" said Granddad.

Adam and Luke cheered, and Granddad grinned as he started the tractor up again and took them for a ride around the farm.

PATIENCE

waiting with a happy heart

"And let us not be weary in well doing, for in due season we shall reap, if we faint not." –Galatians 6:9

The telephone rang, and Mommy answered it and chatted for a few moments. When she hung up, she said with a smile, "Guess what Nana called for?"

"What?" asked Cassidy and Adam together.

"She wanted to see if we could go with her and your cousins to the pumpkin patch," their mom replied. "After that, we'll go out for lunch together. Does that sound like fun?"

"Yay!" Cass squealed. "I can't wait!"

"Awesome!" Adam exclaimed.

“Okay,” said their mom. “I told Nana we can go, but that means we have to be very diligent in getting our schoolwork done this morning. We only have an hour till we need to leave.”

Adam and Cassidy opened their schoolbooks again, but soon Cassidy looked up and asked, “How much longer now, Mommy?”

“Only an hour, Cass,” her mom said. “But I want you both to be patient. You need to pay attention to your schoolwork, and you won’t be able to do that unless you practice patience. Then the time will go by faster, too!”

“Okay, Mommy,” said Cass.

“Do you remember what patience is?” Mommy asked them.

“Patience is waiting with a happy heart!” said Adam.

“That’s right,” said Mom. “Now let’s finish our schoolwork while we wait with happy hearts!”

Cassidy and Adam thought about what their mom said and decided to try their hardest to be patient. Before they knew it, they had finished their pages, and it was time to leave.

“Wow, Mommy!” Cassidy exclaimed as they got in the car. “Patience did make the time go by faster!”

Soon they reached the pumpkin patch, where they met all their cousins and aunts. There they had a fun day as they played on the inflatables, painted pumpkins, and gave each other wagon rides.

“I can’t wait to go get lunch!” Adam declared as he ducked through the door of the Indian teepee.

“Remember patience, Adam,” his mom teased, and they laughed.

“I know what,” said Adam. “I’ll wait patiently with a happy heart, and maybe that will make the time go faster till we go to the restaurant!”

HONESTY

always giving a truthful answer

"Lie not to one another." –Colossians 3:9

"The end," said Mommy, as she closed the book she had just finished reading to Cassidy and Adam. "Can we read another, Mommy?" asked Cassidy. "Please?"

"I would love to read another to you," said Mommy, "but Daddy is going to be home soon and I need to get dinner started. You may read some yourself, or if you want to wait, we can read together as a family after dinner."

"I'll read some more by myself," decided Cassidy. "I love *Little House* books!"

"I don't want to read anymore," said Adam, getting up and heading to his room. "I'm gonna go play farm."

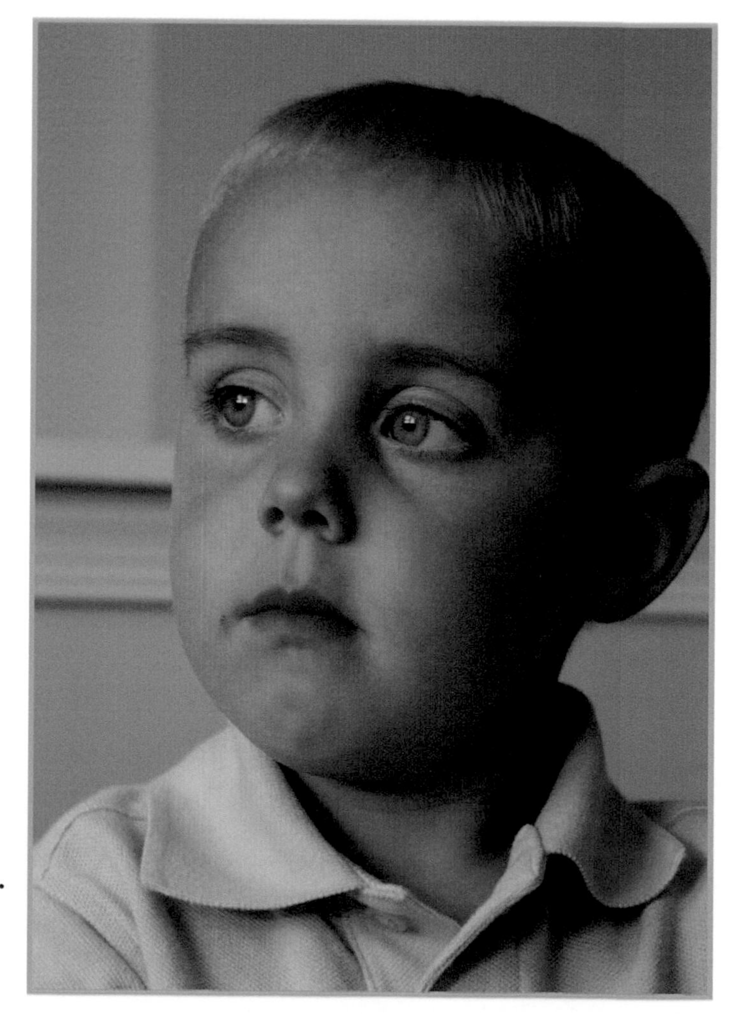

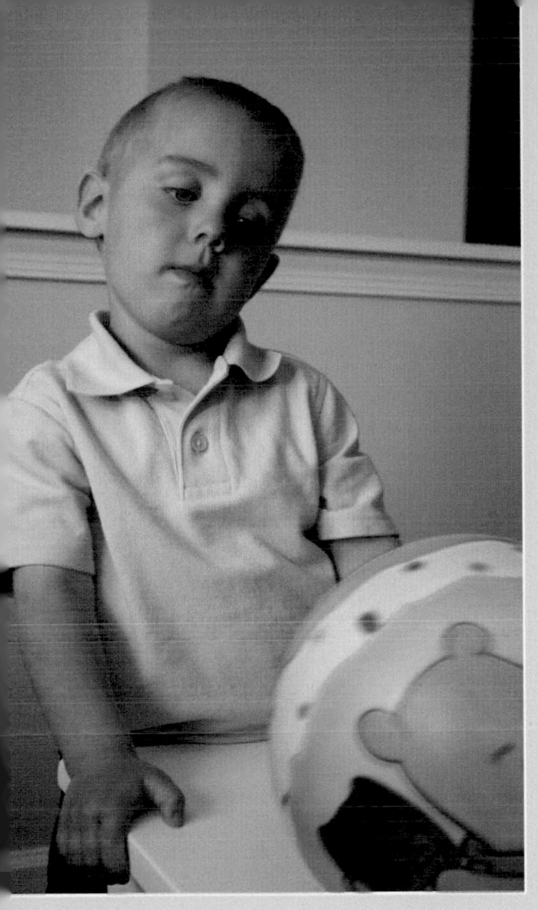

Adam played with his toy barn and farm animals for awhile, but grew tired of them and looked around for something else to do. Spying a bouncy ball on the toy shelf, he grabbed it and amused himself first by trying to use one of Cassidy's teacups as a hoop for the ball, and then by bouncing it on the floor. Higher and higher it bounced. Adam was delighted when it bounced as high as the door. He bounced it harder.

CRASH! The ball hit the light on the ceiling fan and shattered the bulb and light fixture.

"Oh, no!" thought Adam. "I didn't mean to bounce it that hard!"

Adam's mom had heard the crash and came in. "What was that, Adam? Are you okay?" she asked. Then she saw the broken glass. "What happened, son?"

"Um," gulped Adam, looking guilty. "I, um… well…."

"Please make sure you tell me the truth, Adam," his mom said seriously. "I understand that accidents happen, and I won't punish you for accidentally breaking the light. But you'll always get punished for lying because it is a serious sin."

"Well," said Adam, clearing his throat. "I'm sorry, Mommy. I was bouncing the ball and I wanted to see how high it would go, but I didn't mean to break the light."

"Okay, son," said his mom. "I'm so glad you chose to be honest. God wants us to always, always, always tell the truth!"

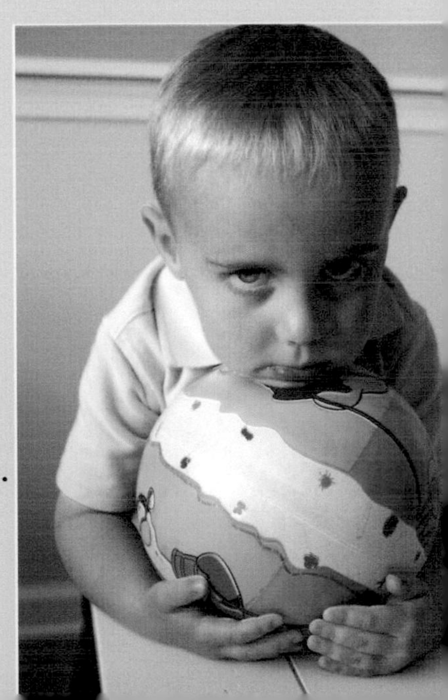

GRATEFULNESS

being sure to tell God and others thank you

"Giving thanks ALWAYS for ALL things unto God and the Father, in the name of our Lord Jesus Christ." –Ephesians 5:20

"Wake up, Anne!" whispered her mom. "Today is the day Nana is taking you shopping!"

Anne rubbed her eyes sleepily, sat up and looked at her mom. "Oh!" she said, suddenly remembering. "I'd better get dressed!"

Nana liked to take each of her grandchildren out for a special time of shopping and lunch every so often, and Anne was looking forward to her date with Nana today!

Anne quickly got dressed while her mom fixed her breakfast. While they were eating, Mommy reminded her, "Remember to show gratefulness for all Nana does for you today, Anne. Tell her thank you for taking you out for a special time today."

"I will," Anne promised.

Soon after breakfast, Nana arrived to pick Anne up. First they went to the toy store, where they spent a lot of time in the dollhouse aisle.

"I love this set of dollhouse people," said Anne,

pointing at a box containing a mom, dad, big brother and big sister, a baby and a dog. "I've never seen this one before!"

"Would you like to have it for your own?" asked Nana. "Let me buy it for you, and then you can play with it whenever you want."

Anne smiled a great big smile, and then she

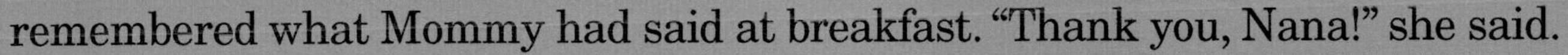

remembered what Mommy had said at breakfast. "Thank you, Nana!" she said.

"You're welcome!" Nana smiled. They bought the set, and then they went to the bookstore where there were lots of books for children to read and toys to play with. Soon their tummies were growling, so Nana decided it was time for lunch. Anne prayed over their meal, thanking God for her food and adding, "And thank You that I got to come with Nana today and for all the special things she does for me."

After they ate, Nana suggested they have ice cream cones for dessert. "What kind of ice cream would you like, Anne?" she asked.

"Could I have bubble gum ice cream, please?" Anne requested.

"Sure," said Nana, as she placed their orders.

Nana and Anne enjoyed their ice cream together. Afterward, it was time for Anne to go home.

"I had a great time, Nana," Anne said as Nana drove her home. "Thank you so much for taking me shopping and out for lunch and ice cream and dollhouse people!"

"You're welcome, Anne," smiled Nana. "And thank you for showing gratefulness!"

RESPECTFULNESS

treating others with honor

"Do nothing from selfishness or empty conceit, but with humility of mind let each of you regard one another as more important than himself." –Philippians 2:3b NASB

It was nearly suppertime, and Lauren's mom and dad were going out for dinner. Lauren could hardly wait for Aunt Emmy to arrive to babysit her while they were gone. It was so much fun when Emmy came! And Mommy said that they could make homemade play dough while she was gone!

Lauren didn't have to wait long. Soon Aunt Emmy's car pulled into the driveway, and Lauren bounced to the door to meet her and give her a big hug.

Mommy showed Aunt Emmy what to have for dinner and gave her instructions about bedtime. "Okay, Lauren," said Mommy, "we're leaving now. Remember to obey whatever Emmy tells you to do, and remember how we've been talking about respectfulness today? Make sure you treat

Aunt Emmy with honor!" "All right, Mommy!" Lauren answered, and waved as Mommy and Daddy got into their car and drove away.

Aunt Emmy prepared dinner, and she and Lauren ate while they talked about what they would play afterward. Lauren wanted to show Emmy her dollhouse and play kitchen. After they ate, Lauren ran to her room and showed Aunt Emmy all her toys. Then they had a snack in the kitchen, and soon Aunt Emmy said it was bedtime. Lauren frowned.

"I don't think my mom would make me go to bed yet," she said.

"Remember, Lauren, your mom said to obey me," Emmy gently reminded her. "If you disobey me, you're disobeying her too. You're not being very respectful right now."

Lauren was tempted to be angry. She was having so much fun that she did not want to go to bed. But she remembered that Mommy and Daddy told her to treat Aunt Emmy respectfully while they were gone, and she knew it would not be fun if Emmy told them she had disobeyed. So Lauren whispered, "Dear Jesus, I don't want to go to bed, but I want to obey Mommy and Daddy. Please help me do what is right." Then she took a deep breath and smiled at Aunt Emmy. "I'm sorry, Aunt Emmy," she said. "I'll obey and let you help me get ready for bed now."

"Good girl," Aunt Emmy smiled. "And I'll give your mom and dad a good report about you!" Lauren grinned and Aunt Emmy gave her a hug as they headed down the hall.

RESPONSIBILITY

doing my best at every job because Jesus is watching

"And whatsoever ye do, do it heartily, as unto the Lord, and not unto men." –Colossians 3:23

Cassidy was excited that her schoolwork was finished for the day so that she could go play outside. Excitedly she ran toward the front door, when she heard her mom calling her.

"Yes, Mommy?" she answered.

"Cass, you need to clean your room before you play outside," Mommy told her. Cassidy obediently went to her room to clean, but when she saw how many toys were on the floor, she sighed. "This will take forever!" she thought to herself with disappointment. "I'll never get to play outside!"

Cassidy slowly put away her dolls and began gathering up her doll clothes when an idea came to her mind. "I know!" she thought silently. "I'll just push all these things under the bed, and then Mommy will think I cleaned it all up and I can play outside much faster!"

Cassidy started shoving her dolls' dresses under the bed, but then she stopped as she thought of her family's devotions the night before. "Last night, Daddy told us that responsibility means doing every job as if Jesus were watching me," she remembered. "Jesus is watching me, and He cares if I practice responsibility."

Cassidy pulled the clothes back out and began putting them away properly. She felt relieved and happy that she had chosen to do right. She began humming to herself, and before she knew it, her room was all clean!

Mommy came into her room. "Good job, Cassidy!" she praised her. "Your room looks very tidy. You didn't see me, but I was watching you when you started putting things

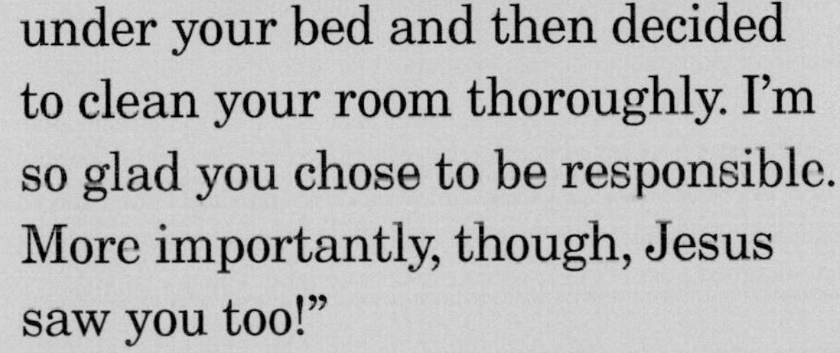

under your bed and then decided to clean your room thoroughly. I'm so glad you chose to be responsible. More importantly, though, Jesus saw you too!"

"I know," Cassidy nodded with a smile. "I thought about family devotions last night, and that's why I decided to clean the right way."

"I'm proud of you, honey," said Mommy, giving her a hug. "And now you may go play outside!"

INITIATIVE

meeting a need without being asked

"Whatsoever thy hand findeth to do, do it with thy might." –Ecclesiastes 9:10

Cassidy was very excited. She had been waiting a long time for this day to arrive. Her mom had planned a special tea party for her and her girl cousins, and the day was finally here! She could hardly wait to see her cousins!

Cass had helped her mom make a yummy dip to eat with fruit. She was helping her arrange the other snacks on the plates when the baby started crying, and Mommy went to take care of him.

"What else needs to be done?" Cassidy wondered, realizing her mom might need some help since the baby was already awake. Cassidy looked around and noticed her mom hadn't gotten a chance to set the table yet, so she began to set the table with her pretty teaset and dishes.

Next Cassidy noticed there were still some toys out in the living room that Adam had forgotten to put away before he left to run errands with Daddy, so without being asked, she took the toys to the bedroom and put them away. When Mommy returned to the room fifteen minutes later, she was relieved when she saw how much Cassidy had gotten done.

"Thank you so much, Cassidy," she said, "for taking the initiative to get so much done for me. I couldn't get everything done that I needed to while I was taking care of your brother, and you have saved me a lot of time and helped so much to get ready for the party!"

"Glad to do it!" smiled Cassidy. "It was fun. What else can I do to help?"

Just then the doorbell rang. Mommy smiled and said, "I'll make sure everything is ready in the kitchen. I think the only other thing I need you to do is just open the door and greet your aunts and cousins!"

"I'd love to!" laughed Cassidy, and she ran to do just that.

DILIGENCE

doing my very best at every task given to me

"Whether therefore ye eat, or drink, or whatsoever ye do, do all to the glory of God." –I Corinthians 10:31

Lauren and her mommy were baking chocolate chip cookies. Lauren loved to help her mom bake, and she especially loved chocolate chip cookies. Mommy let Lauren help measure the sugar and butter.

"May I crack an egg, Mommy?" Lauren asked.

"Okay, honey. Remember to be careful not to let any shells get in the bowl," Mommy said, as she handed her an egg. Lauren carefully cracked the egg into the bowl. Mommy turned the mixer on. Soon it was time to add the flour.

"May I put the flour in, Mommy?" Lauren asked.

"Sure, honey," Mommy replied, measuring flour into a cup. She handed the cup of flour to Lauren, and Lauren turned it upside down over the bowl. Some of the flour missed the bowl, however, and spilled onto the counter and the floor below.

"Oh dear," said Lauren. "I made a mess!"

"That's okay; we'll just clean it up. You can help," said Mommy.

Lauren ran to get her little broom, and Mommy got the big broom. Together they swept the floor. Lauren carefully swept all the flour off the floor and into the dustpan. Then she swept that spot on the floor again, just to make sure she had gotten it all.

"Great job, Lauren!" Mommy praised her when they finished. "You were very diligent in cleaning up the flour so thoroughly. I'm proud of you!"

Lauren smiled. "It feels good to be diligent," she said. "I know God is watching what I do, and I want to do a good job for Him!"

"That makes Mommy and Daddy very happy," her mom said with a smile. Lauren smiled back. "Is it time to put the chocolate chips in now?" she asked.

"It sure is! Would you like to do it?" her mom asked.

"Yes, I would!" Lauren beamed. This was her favorite part! They stirred in the chocolate chips and then spooned the cookie dough onto the cookie sheets.

"How long do they need to bake?" asked Lauren.

"About ten minutes," said her mom. "While we're waiting, we can do the dishes."

"Okay!" said Lauren. "And we can practice being diligent again!"

"All right," her mom said with a smile, as she slid the cookie sheet into the oven. "And when we're done, we'll have some nice, warm cookies!"

KINDNESS

treating others as you would like to be treated by them (realizing they belong to God)

"And as ye would that men should do to you, do ye also to them likewise." –Luke 6:31

Lauren and Luke were at their Nana and Granddad's house with their cousins. The children were doing flips or special tricks, taking turns so no one would get hurt.

Luke did his trick and then got off the trampoline and went to stand at the end of the line behind Lauren, waiting for his turn to come again. Lauren was excited for her turn to come, and as she looked at four of her cousins in line ahead of her, she sighed, thinking, "I'll have to wait several more minutes before I get to take a turn!"

Luke was so excited that he couldn't stop talking about what his next trick was going to be. "Lauren," he said, "I'm going to try for my

highest jump ever, and then I'm going to try to do a flip in mid-air! Oh, I can't waaaaaaait for my next turn!"

Lauren smiled and then she had a thought. "Mommy said that I should always treat others as I want them to treat me," she said to herself. "I think I'll choose to be kind and let Luke take my turn."

Lauren slipped out of line and went to stand behind Luke. "There, Luke," she said kindly. "I'll switch turns with you. I know you're really excited about trying your new jump."

"Thanks, Lauren!" cried Luke excitedly. "Thank you so much for being kind! I really appreciate it!" Lauren smiled. "You're welcome," she said. "I can't wait to see you try your new jump!"

SELF-CONTROL

controlling my desires to be more like Jesus

"He that hath no rule over his spirit is like a city that is broken down, and without walls." –Proverbs 25:28

Luke was playing outside on a warm, late autumn morning. He decided to ride his bike, so he went to the shed where it was kept, opened the door and walked over to his bike. Only then did he realize one of the tires was flat.

Luke was very disappointed. He stomped inside, pouting, and slammed the door.

"What's the matter, Luke?" his mom asked.

"I'm very angry because I wanted to ride my bike, but the tire is flat!" Luke said crossly.

"Luke, you need to use self control even when disappointing things happen," his mom instructed him. "Being

angry and losing your temper won't fix anything. When I'm finished folding the laundry, I'll see if I can find the bike pump and put some more air in your tire. Until then, please play with Melody so I can finish my work."

Luke started walking over to Melody. Then he dropped down to his hands and knees and began to roar and growl, crawling towards her as he did so. Melody wailed, "Luke, stop!" but Luke continued towards her.

"Luke," Mommy asked, "do you think Melody likes that?"

"I'm just playing, Mommy," Luke told her.

"I know, but your sister isn't enjoying it as

much as you are. Please be considerate of her and stop teasing her."

Luke sighed and looked around for something to play with. He spotted one of his toy trucks. Running over to it, he picked it up and began making loud truck noises as he pushed it toward the tower of blocks Melody was building.

"Watch out, Mel!" he shouted. "Here comes my monster truck, and it's out of control!" He crashed the car into the tower, and the blocks came tumbling down.

"Luke!" cried Melody. "You destroyed my tower!"

Mommy came over and instructed Luke to ask Melody's forgiveness. "Luke," she said quietly, "I think you need some practice in exercising self-control. I want you to sit on the couch for ten minutes without talking. You can pray silently and ask Jesus to help you control your desires so you can be more like Him. When the timer rings, you can get up and try again to play while using self-control."

Luke sat on the sofa and Mommy set the timer. Luke thought soberly, "This isn't much fun. It's kind of hard to use self-control, but I think it's worth it." Then he bowed his head to ask God to help him be more like Jesus. When the timer rang and Mommy told him he could get up, he went over to Melody and gave her a hug. "I'm sorry, Mel," he said. "My lack of self-control caused you irritation. Will you forgive me?"

"Sure, Luke!" said Melody, and she hugged him back. "Now can I play monster trucks with you?"

"Of course!" grinned Luke, and they sat down together to play. "And this time I'll use self-control!"

CONTENTMENT

knowing God has given me everything I need to be happy

"For I have learned in whatsoever state I am, therewith to be content." –Philippians 4:11b

Anne was very excited that she was going to play with her cousins at Nana's house. The girls loved playing dollhouse together, and Anne was bringing along the dollhouse family that Nana had bought her at the toy store recently.

When Anne got to Nana's house, her cousins were already there, so all the girls headed downstairs play dollhouse.

"Look, Cassidy," said Anne, "see my new family?"

"Oh, Anne, these are so sweet!" said Cassidy. "Look at the little baby, sucking her thumb! I love them!"

"Thanks," said Anne. Lauren and Melody crowded around to see Anne's new people, too. "Pretty!" said Lauren.

Melody admired them, and they all began playing with Nana. Nana had several dollhouses, so each girl could usually have her own, and lots of people, pets,

furniture and cars to go along with them. The girls never grew tired of playing dollhouse with Nana!

Anne began setting up the furniture. When she had it arranged the way she liked it, she put her people inside and began looking around for the vehicles.

"Nana, where is the convertible?" she asked.

"I think Melody's playing with it," Nana answered. "Would you like this van instead?"

"Well," said Anne, "I was really hoping to play with the convertible, actually."

Just then, Anne's mom came downstairs. Anne explained to her that she wanted the car that Melody was playing with.

"But Mel has it, honey," said Mommy. "Play with another one. Look, there are plenty of cars for everyone."

Anne looked sad. Mommy pulled her aside and said gently, "Anne, you should really be content with what you have. You have a dollhouse to yourself, all the furniture you wanted, and a brand new set of people from Nana. There are plenty of other cars to choose from. Melody chose hers first, so be content to settle for another one. Do you remember what contentment is, Anne?" Mommy continued.

Anne nodded. "Contentment is knowing God has given me everything I need to be happy," she answered.

"That's right," said Mommy. "So why don't you go back to playing with your cousins and choose to be happy with what God has given you?"

"Okay, Mommy," said Anne with a smile. "I'll choose to be content!"

DEFERENCE (SHARING)

giving others first choice because they are special to God

"The generous soul will be made rich and he who waters will also be watered himself." –Proverbs 11:25

"Mommy, look!" Luke exclaimed as he rushed through the front door. "I was out playing in the yard, and Mrs. Conn gave me some candy!"

Mommy looked up from her crocheting. "Well, that was kind of her! That's a big box of candy!"

"Yes, it is," Luke said excitedly. "I'll share them with you and with Mel, Mommy!"

"That's so kind of you, Luke," said his mom. "Thank you for sharing!"

Melody gave Luke a big hug.

Luke grinned, taking the lid off. "Look, Mommy, Mrs. Conn made this herself, and it's fudge that has one chocolate layer and one peanut butter layer!"

"Ooh, that looks delicious!" said his mom.

"Here you go," said Luke, giving each of them a piece. "One for you, Mommy, and one for you, Mel. And one for me," he added, popping one into his mouth. "And I'll save some for Daddy, so he can have some when he gets home."

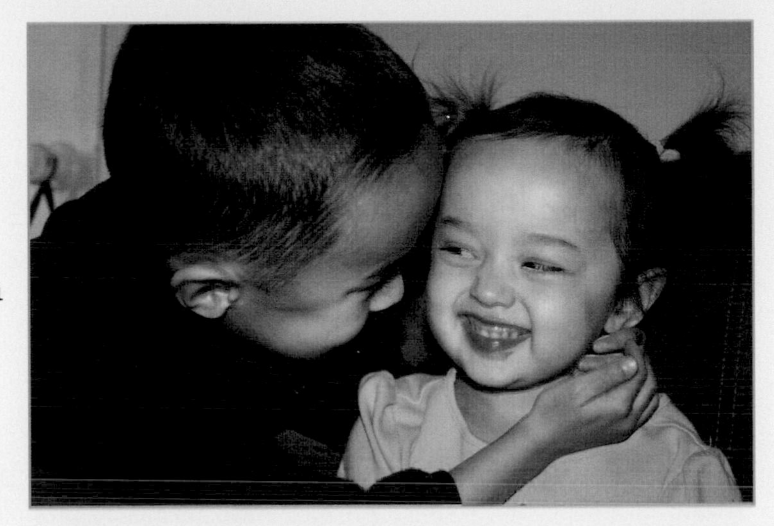

"Thanks for the candy! I am proud of you for sharing so willingly, Luke," his mom told him.

"You're welcome," said Luke. "I actually think it's more fun to share. If I kept it all for myself, I might be happy, but when I share, all three of us are happy! And that makes it even more fun."